THE LOST DIARY OF
JULIUS CAESAR'S SLAVE

THE LOST DIARY OF JULIUS CAESAR'S SLAVE

DISCOVERED BY
STEVE BARLOW & STEVE SKIDMORE
ILLUSTRATED BY GEORGE HOLLINGSWORTH

Other Lost Diaries recently discovered

The Lost Diary of Tutankhamun's Mummy
The Lost Diary of Erik Bloodaxe, Viking Warrior

Text copyright © 1997 by Steve Barlow and Steve Skidmore.
Cover illustration copyright © 1997 by Martin Chatterton.
Illustrations copyright © 1997 by George Hollingsworth.

Published by Troll Communications L.L.C.

This paperback edition published in 1999. Published by arrangement with HarperCollins Publishers Ltd.

The author and illustrator assert the moral right to be recognized as the author and illustrator of this work.

Printed in the United States of America.

10 9 8 7 6 5 4 3 2 1

MESSAGE TO READERS

We have been concerned by the arguments that have raged since the publication of the first Lost Diaries. Expert historians, while agreeing that the books are historically accurate, say that:

• they cannot find any evidence that the characters who are supposed to have written the Lost Diaries ever actually existed;

• the Lost Diaries refer to things such as telephone hotlines that weren't invented until centuries later.

Therefore, when we heard that Barlow and Skidmore claimed to have discovered the Lost Diary of a British captive who became Julius Caesar's personal slave, we were naturally cautious.

This time, however, Barlow and Skidmore have been able to produce a letter stating that the diary is completely genuine. The letter explains that the diary of Commonus Muccus was discovered during a dig by the famous archaeologists Sir Liesalot and his French partner, Le Duc à L'Orange. The letter is signed by an international panel of experts: Doctor "Doc" Bill de Platypus and Professor G. Day-Sport of the University of Wugga Wugga, Australia; Professor Donna Kebab of the Athens Department of Antiquities; Professor Harvey Nice-Day of the Smithsonian Institute; Professor Wendy Sainsgo-Marchinin of UCLA in California; and Doctor Willie Orwontee of the University of Nairobi, Kenya.

We are delighted, therefore, to be able to publish this exciting and ABSOLUTELY AUTHENTIC account of the last days of the Roman Republic, *The Lost Diary of Julius Caesar's Slave*.

R S L C
(ROMAN SLAVE LICENSING CENTER)
<u>SLAVE REGISTRATION DOCUMENT</u>

REGISTERED KEEPER OF THE SLAVE: GAIUS JULIUS CAESAR

DATE OF REGISTRATION: 57 BC

NAME OF SLAVE: COMMONUS MUCCUS

PREVIOUS NAME: COMMONIX

REGISTRATION MARK: "JC" BRANDED ON ARM

TYPE OF SLAVE: PRIVATE/LIGHT GOODS

COUNTRY OF MANUFACTURE: BRITTANIA

PLACE OF MANUFACTURE: COUNTRY OF THE DUMNONII

YEAR OF MANUFACTURE: 85 BC

COLORING: DARK HAIR, BROWN EYES

PREVIOUS KEEPER: SCIATICA (WIFE), THE HOVEL, DUMNONIISHIRE

IF YOU SELL THIS SLAVE TO SOMEONE ELSE,
YOU MUST NOTIFY THE RSLC.

I have to carry this piece of paper with me everywhere I go now, or I get a beating. Stupid Roman regulations!

What have I done to deserve this? Don't these Romans know that Britons never, never, never shall be slaves? I'd just come over to Gaul* for a quick visit to my cousin Horlix, but no sooner had I stepped ashore than some Romans pounced on me and dragged me off. They took me to their General, Julius Caesar. Next thing I know, I've got his initials burned into my arm (boy, did that hurt!). He gave me a new name and told me I'm his personal slave and I'd better do as I'm told or else.

I don't know what Sciatica will say. Well, I do. She'll say, "Where have you been? Do you know what time it is? Oh, you've been with the Roman army, have you? All right, tell the truth. What have you been up to?"

I've decided to keep a diary so I can show it to Sciatica when I get home—to prove where I've been.

If I ever do get home, that is.

*France

- 57 BC -

Northern Gaul

Julius Caesar (JC, as we slaves call him) is in charge of the Roman army here in Gaul*.

He's just a little fellow with a big nose, but his soldiers think he's the best thing since roasted rodents. The reason is, he fights like one of them.

Most Roman generals stay well out of harm's way when there's a battle raging. They live in luxurious tents, drinking the finest wines and pigging out on fancy food, while their men are starving and boiling their sandals to eat.

* Julius Caesar's own record of the conquest of Gaul makes it clear that in 57 BC, the Roman Legions were fighting the Belgians—Gallic tribes who lived in what is now Belgium.

The soldiers I've talked to say JC doesn't do that. He fights at the front with his men, and when they go hungry, he goes hungry too. In the last battle they had with the Gauls, the legions were getting badly beaten until JC joined in, calling all his men by name and chopping away like a maniac. The legionnaires say they fight twice as hard for him as they would for anyone else.

It's not too tough, being a slave. All I have to do is hang around until JC wants something, then I get it for him. It'd be a great job, if I got paid for it. I wonder if Sciatica is missing me?

We're on the move. JC is marching with the legions, and he's sent me back to the baggage train. Some guy offered me a ride on his cart. It turns out his name's Inkus Fingus, and he's one of JC's clerks. He's okay—for a Roman.

This army is really organized! Back home, the chiefs give the orders and everyone does what they're told, more or less. When we march we just trudge along any old way.

In the Roman army, they march in neat rows; cavalry first, then foot soldiers, with scouts riding out to look for ambushes. The people who give the orders are called officers. Every ten men have an officer called a Decurion, and for every hundred men there's a Centurion. The ordinary soldiers are called legionnaires because they don't belong to tribes, they belong to legions, such as the Third Legion and the Fifth Legion, and so on.

People even volunteer to be in the army. Inkus showed me one of their recruiting posters—very persuasive!

YOUR ARMY NEEDS YOU!
SEE THE WORLD AND CONQUER IT!

ARE YOU A ROMAN CITIZEN?
DO YOU HAVE GOOD EYESIGHT AND HEARING?
CAN YOU READ AND WRITE? ARE YOU OVER 5 FEET (1.6 M) TALL?

YES?

JOIN THE PROFESSIONALS:
BECOME A LEGIONNAIRE!

JOIN THE ARMY AND SEE THE WORLD.
YOUR CHANCE TO PROFIT — LOOTING IS ENCOURAGED!
MONEY, ANIMALS, AND SLAVES ARE ALL YOURS TO KEEP OR SELL!
WHEN YOU RETIRE WE GIVE YOU A PIECE OF LAND AND A PENSION.
BE THE OBJECT OF RESPECT.
GOOD CAREER PROSPECTS — BECOME A CENTURION.
BATTLE THE BARBARIANS!
LEARN A TRADE!
IN TODAY'S MODERN LEGION, YOU CAN LEARN TO:
DIG DITCHES . . . BUILD FORTS . . . MAKE ROADS.

THE SMALL PRINT
You have to join up for 25 years!
You pay for your uniform, weapons, and food out of your wages.
We keep some of your wages and give them back to you when you retire (if you live that long).
Discipline is strict! (We're talking VERY, VERY strict.)
You must like marching—up to 19 miles (30 km) a day.

The baggage train with the camping equipment, food, and spare weapons follows the soldiers. It stretches for miles! Then there are all the people who follow the legion: doctors, engineers, cooks, clerks, priests, surveyors. Some of the legionnaires even have wives and kids tagging along, and slaves of course.

Inkus Fingus has been telling me about my new boss. Caesar sounds like a pretty clever guy.

All top Romans have to be good at soldiering and good at politics. Some of them are good generals and lousy politicians, some of them are lousy generals but good politicians. Inkus says JC is a good general *and* a good politician, and that's why he's in Gaul.

When JC was in Rome, he was elected Consul

(that's like a chief) along with two of his buddies named Pompey and Crassus. They were called the Triumvirate because there were three of them. Pompey was more powerful than JC because years ago he fought wars in the East and conquered new territories for Rome. Inkus thinks JC really wants to be boss of Rome on his own, but first he has to make a name for himself. That's why he left the Triumvirate and got himself elected Proconsul of Gaul. He wants to conquer Gaul and make it part of the Roman Empire.

Strangely enough, the Gauls aren't all that excited about the idea. At the moment it's the Belgians who are causing trouble, so that's who the Romans are fighting.

I asked Inkus why JC wanted me as his personal slave. He said, "Because nobody else has a Briton as a personal slave."

I said that was a stupid reason.

Inkus said, "Not to JC, it isn't. He has to be first with everything."

When I climbed up on the cart this morning,
I found a scrap of paper
stuck to the horse's rump.
This is what it said:

ARTUS DALUS INC.
SLAVE DEALERS
TO THE ARISTOCRACY

TOP BRANDS AT LOW, LOW PRICES

SLAVES BOUGHT, SOLD,
RENOVATED, AND SERVICED

YOUR OLD SLAVES WANTED
IN ANY CONDITION—
FIT, TIRED, OR BARELY BREATHING!

LEGIONNAIRES:
SELL YOUR SLAVES THROUGH US!
GOOD PRICES PAID,
NO QUESTIONS ASKED.

LOCAL AGENTS:
DELUS BOYUS AND RODDUS

Inkus Fingus explained that there were always slave dealers following the army because when legionnaires captured prisoners of war, they would sell them as slaves. This meant the legionnaires didn't have to feed the prisoners or prevent them from escaping.

I asked, casually, what would happen to a slave who was caught trying to run away. Inkus gave a lopsided grin and told me all about the games in the Circus Maximus. He said that slaves who had run away, or whose masters didn't want them anymore, were always popular in the Circus Maximus.

"What do they do?" I asked. "Juggle?"

"They get torn apart by wild beasts."

Wonderful, I thought. What am I going to do? There's no point in trying to escape. I haven't got a clue where I am, and there are Romans all over the place. I suppose I'll just have to stay on JC's good side, or it'll be Circus time!

Namur,* Gaul

We're camped out outside a fortress occupied by some Gauls called the Atuacui. Our engineers have built a giant siege tower to attack the walls of the fort. The Atuacui just jeered at first, shouting insulting comments from their walls like "Get a life," but they started laughing on the other side of their faces when the tower kept growing until it was higher than their walls.

* The exact location of this fort is uncertain, but the Atuacui were a Belgian tribe in the Ardennes region, which is in the southeastern part of modern Belgium.

INSIDE:
WE REVIEW THE
LATEST MOVIES!
SEAN CONNERIX IS
JAMES BOND, 007,
IN *GAULFINGER*

ELVIS PRESLIX IN *GAULS! GAULS! GAULS!*

The Gauldian
ATUACUI ATTACK!

Caesar's legions suffered a serious setback last night when the Atuacui tribe broke out of its stronghold of Namur, in spite of the fact that the tribal leaders had already agreed to surrender to the Roman army. The Atuacui, using weapons they had kept hidden, stormed the powerful Roman defenses, and a savage battle has been reported. Tonight, all Gaul holds its breath as the gallant Belgians fight on.

LATE NEWS
Belgians Routed
The brave Belgian defenders of Namur have been defeated. The Roman general, Julius Caesar, rallied his legions to beat off their attack. Sources indicate that over 4,000 Belgians were killed.

After the battle, JC sent for Delus Boyus and told him he was going to sell him all the inhabitants of Namur.

Delus's eyes nearly popped out. "*All* of them?" he asked.

JC said, "Yes, all of them."

Delus rubbed his hands together. "Profitus Maximus," he cackled. (That's the name of his chief slave-master.) "We'll have a sale."

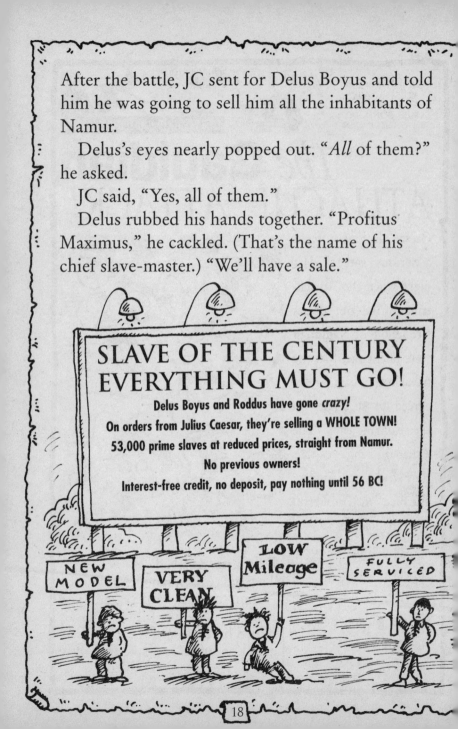

SLAVE OF THE CENTURY
EVERYTHING MUST GO!

Delus Boyus and Roddus have gone *crazy*!

On orders from Julius Caesar, they're selling a WHOLE TOWN!

53,000 prime slaves at reduced prices, straight from Namur.

No previous owners!

Interest-free credit, no deposit, pay nothing until 56 BC!

NEW MODEL

VERY CLEAN

LOW Mileage

FULLY SERVICED

The Belgians have been very quiet since the battle at Namur. Officially, only Cisalpina Gaul and Transalpina Gaul* belong to Rome, but JC wants to control all of Gaul.** The chiefs of all the tribes pay tribute to Rome, because they know if they don't, the legions will give them a good drubbing.

Rome is just a city, not a country, but it's the center of a huge Empire. The legions created the Roman Empire, and they keep it going.

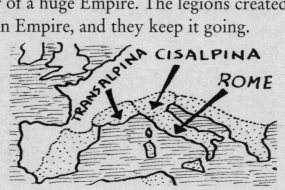

Anyone who wants a top job in Rome has to have the legions on his side. Inkus Fingus says JC's not allowed to go back to Rome while he's Proconsul of Gaul, because if he showed up in Rome with his legions behind him, he could take over the city. Instead, he's having a meeting with some important bigwigs from Rome at some place called Lucca, and I'm going too—to carry the bags.

* The province of Gaul consisted at this time of the north of Italy (Cisalpina Gaul) and southern France (Transalpina Gaul).
** Between 58 BC and 51 BC, Julius Caesar gradually added to his conquests until the province of Gaul included all of modern France and Belgium.

Lucca, Cisalpina Gaul

Inkus Fingus had already told me about the Triumvirate when we were marching. They're the bigwigs who came from Rome. Well, now that I've seen them, I hope the gods are watching out for Rome with those three in charge.

First, there's Pompey. He looks like a boxer who's past his prime. He's married to JC's daughter. (That should give you some idea of how ruthless JC is. He'd marry his daughter off to an old toad like Pompey just so he's a member of the family and easier to handle.) Pompey was Rome's best general before JC came along, but now he's fat and lazy, and I'd guess he's not happy that the legions that once cheered for him are now cheering for JC.

Still, he's not as jealous as Crassus. Crassus has never been a general, or anything much except filthy rich. You can tell he hates JC.

The third of the group is Clodius, who got the job because JC wasn't allowed to be in the Triumvirate *and* be Proconsul of Gaul. Clodius is nothing but a gangster. Groups of his thugs roam around Rome beating people up and stealing things.

Put them all together, and you've got as nasty a collection of pond life as you'd find anywhere.

We've had a week of Pompey and company, with everyone giving false smiles and patting each other on the back (no doubt looking for somewhere to stick a knife in). I think they're all out to get JC, and he knows it too. He's got a little stuffed bear he takes to bed, and he lies there cuddling it. He thinks nobody knows, but I've seen it. I've heard him whisper things like, "They're all out to get me, Teddus," and "Teddus, you're my only friend." Then he falls asleep with his thumb in his mouth.

Thankfully, Pompey, Crassus, and Clodius are leaving for Rome today, and JC's going to straighten out some trouble in the North.

This trouble all started with the Venetii.* They've been good friends with my tribe, the Dumnonii, for years. The Venetii are great sailors, and they carry tin from mines in my country to trade with Rome. My cousin Horlix married a Venetii woman and went to live in Gaul—I was on my way to see him when the Romans captured me.

Anyway, apparently the Venetii have refused to pay taxes and they've taken some Roman officers hostage, so we're marching tomorrow. I'll be cheering for the Venetii, of course, only very quietly so JC doesn't hear me.

* One of the Gaulish tribes living in the part of France now called Brittany

The Gauldian

ALL OF GAUL LOVES OUR SAILORS!

The Venetii navy sets sail today to challenge Julius Caesar's great fleet. As he prepared to sail, Venetii fleet captain Titanix told *The Gauldian*, "Our ships are bigger than anything those Romans have, our sailors are the best in Gaul, and we know the waters around our own coast. It'll be a massacre."

LATE NEWS
Venetii navy sunk

Today, the battle of Quiberon Bay has ended in disaster for the Gallic navy. The Venetii ships, which are bigger and a lot more seaworthy, were outmaneuvered by the faster Roman galleys. The Romans disabled the Venetii vessels by cutting their ropes with sickles tied to the ends of poles. When the wind suddenly dropped, even the ships that still had sails were helpless against the Roman ships, which were powered by oars. Tonight, every single ship in the powerful Venetii navy has been either captured or sunk.

Brittany, Gaul

JC said the Venetii were rebels. He had all the leaders executed, and the rest of the people were sold to Delus Boyus and Roddus, who were hanging around like vultures as usual.

I keep wondering about Horlix. Was he on one of the ships, or was he captured and made a slave like me? I didn't see him among the slaves, but maybe I missed him—there were so many of them. I hope he got away.

The Rhine

JC had to march up here quickly when he heard that two German tribes had crossed the Rhine River and were trying to settle in Gaul. Inkus Fingus explained to me that the Rhine is one of the boundaries of the Roman Empire, and the country on the other side is called Germania. Romans don't know much about Germania except that it's full of Germans, but JC does know that he's having enough trouble keeping the Gauls quiet without the Germans joining in, so he wants to send them back where they came from.

I still can't believe what happened today.

While JC and the German chiefs were talking, some hotheads attacked the Roman cavalry. JC wouldn't listen to the Germans' apologies. He ordered the legions to push the Germans back to the Rhine.

But it turned out that the attackers weren't an army, they were just a tribe looking for somewhere to live. Some of these people were warriors, but most of them were women and children, and old grandmas and grandpas.

JC didn't care who they were. He wanted them punished. How can a guy who goes to bed with a teddy bear watch nearly half a million people drown without shedding a tear?

I can't understand it.

JC came storming out of his tent this morning, waving his newspaper around. He was in an intercontinental ballistic tizzy, and guess who was at Ground Zero?

He threw the paper on the ground, so I looked at it after he'd left.

INSIDE:
GAUL OF
THE MONTH
COMPETITION
See sports page.

Soccer
Roundup

The Gauldian

CATO CLOBBERS CAESAR

By our man in Rome, Sandix Gaul

The Senate* met early today to discuss new honors proposed for Gaius Julius Caesar, Proconsul of Gaul, as a result of his latest campaign. However, Caesar's old enemy, Cato, spoke up and argued that Caesar had attacked innocent people without any warning on the Rhine River. Cato even said that the Senate should hand Caesar over to the Germans for some serious punishment.

After lengthy debate, the motion to give new honors to Caesar was defeated.

* The Roman government

JC's determined to defy the Senate and fight the Germans. He's built a bridge 1,640 feet (500 m) long and over 40 feet (12 m) wide across the Rhine. The legions built it in ten days.

We've been marching up and down the German bank of the Rhine for a couple of weeks. I've been a nervous wreck. Nobody in his right mind tangles with the Germans. German warriors rip your head off and spit down your neck *first*, and *then* ask if you'd like to surrender.

But when the Germans started to gather in force, even JC realized it was time to retreat, so he hurried back over the bridge and chopped it down behind him.

I couldn't see the point of the German expedition until I came across JC gazing at a map. All the countries the Romans had conquered were marked in purple, and he'd just filled in a little bit in Germania.

"You know what, Commonus?" he said dreamily. "No Roman has ever crossed the Rhine before. Never."

I suppose I must not have looked too impressed, because he went on, "When I was thirty-two years old, I went to Spain. There I visited the temple of Hercules in Cádiz. I knelt down before the statue of Alexander the Great, and I wept."

"Did you scrape your knees?" I asked sympathetically.

"NO!" he shouted. "I wept because I was already older than Alexander was when he died. He had conquered the world and I had done nothing. I vowed in that moment that I would make my name as great as Alexander's before my death."

"Very nice," I said. "Very uplifting. Would you like some cocoa?"

JC's up to something, but I don't know what. He's got all his officers running around like their pants are on fire, and all the legions are being supplied with new weapons.

WeaponsRUs Inc.
—ALL THE LATEST WEAPONS—

6 CASSIS

4 SCUTUM

1 PILUM

2 PUGIO

3 GLADIUS

5 CALIGAE

Latest designer armor by Armanius Versacius
Body armor types to suit everyone
Mail-linked ring – a lightweight armor
Iron plates on backing leather with matching accessories

1. Javelin 2. Dagger 3. Sword 4. Shield 5. Sandals 6. Helmet

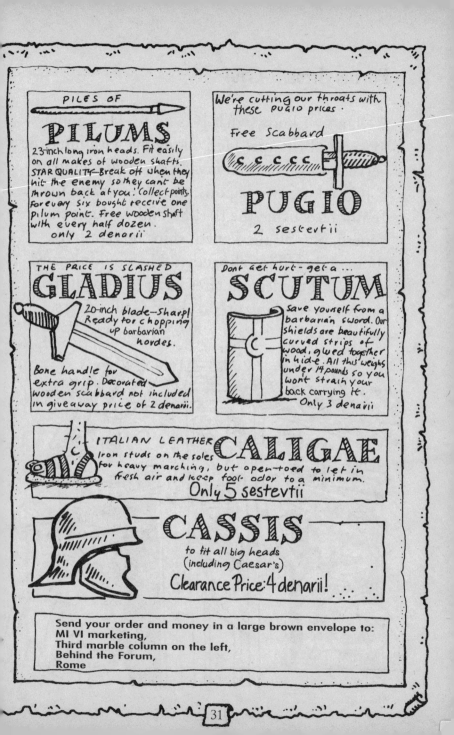

PILES OF

PILUMS

23-inch long iron heads. Fit easily on all makes of wooden shafts. STAR QUALITY—Break off when they hit the enemy so they can't be thrown back at you! Collect points. For every six bought receive one pilum point. Free wooden shaft with every half dozen.
only 2 denarii

We're cutting our throats with these PUGIO prices.

Free Scabbard

PUGIO

2 sestertii

THE PRICE IS SLASHED

GLADIUS

20-inch blade—Sharp! Ready for chopping up barbarian hordes.

Bone handle for extra grip. Decorated wooden scabbard not included in giveaway price of 2 denarii.

Don't get hurt—get a...

SCUTUM

Save yourself from a barbarian sword. Our shields are beautifully curved strips of wood, glued together in hide. All this weighs under 14 pounds so you won't strain your back carrying it.
Only 3 denarii

ITALIAN LEATHER **CALIGAE**
Iron studs on the soles for heavy marching, but open-toed to let in fresh air and keep foot-odor to a minimum.
Only 5 sestertii

CASSIS
to fit all big heads
(including Caesar's)
Clearance Price: 4 denarii!

Portus Itius,* Gaul

Well, now I know what JC's up to. He's going to invade Brittania! He's taking me with him (the nerve!), so I'll have to invade my own country!

JC's taking two legions, the Seventh and the Tenth. He's using the fleet he built to fight the Venetii, plus all the Venetii ships he captured, about eighty ships altogether. He wouldn't need so many if the legionnaires hadn't all spent the past week stocking up on cheap Gallic cigars and drinks.

I asked Inkus Fingus why he thought JC wanted to invade Brittania. He showed me an article in the paper:

CLOTHING SHARES NEWS   Socks up, pants down, hats on top

Business and Finance Gauldian
BOTTOM DROPS OUT OF TIN

World tin prices have reached an all-time high since the sinking of the Venetii fleet last year. When the Venetii ships that carried tin to Rome were all sunk, the supply of tin that came from Cornwall dried up. Rome's stocks of tin are almost exhausted.

Rumors in the city of Rome suggest that Caesar Consolidated Holdings is planning a takeover of the Cornish tin industry.

"So," I said, "it's all just business."

Inkus said, "Yes, mostly. Plus the fact that no Roman has ever been to Brittania before, of course."

"Oh, yes," I said wearily. "There is that."

Brittania

We reached the British coast this morning. I think we must be near Dover. There were big white cliffs above us with Britons lined up on top. They were all wearing nothing but blue paint (called "woad"), shouting, making offensive gestures, and waving their fists at us.* I told JC that this was called woad rage. The Brits would fight until the woad came off, hence the old song "We've come to the end of the woad."

We sailed on to where there weren't any cliffs**, although there were still plenty of Britons yelling rude comments. JC was just about to call the whole thing off when the standard bearer of the Tenth legion shouted out, "Come on, men, the last one ashore's a Gaul." He jumped over the side, and the rest of the legions followed.

Well, I still say it wouldn't have worked if the Britons hadn't been so amazed at these loonies charging up a sloping beach in full armor. They simply forgot to fight and stood watching with their mouths hanging open.

I'm really angry with JC.

Ever since we landed four days ago, he's been strutting around like a peacock. He keeps talking

*When Britons went to war, they painted themselves with blue dye called woad to make themselves feel and look fierce.   ** The Romans actually landed at Deal.

about how easily he beat the Britons, and whenever he and his officers see me, they make clucking noises and burst out laughing.

So I sort of forgot to mention the tides.

Romans aren't used to tides. They don't have them in the Mediterranean. So when JC left his ships beached or bobbing around in the surf like ducks on a pond, it kind of slipped my mind to tell him that it was coming up to full moon and the spring tide, which is the highest tide you can get.

onight, three things happened:
- the cavalry arrived
- the tide came in
- a storm blew up.

And as a result, three things happened:

- the ships on the beach floated away
- the ships at anchor floated until their chains dragged them down, then they filled with water and sank . . . except for those that broke their cables and drifted away
- the cavalry was blown back to Gaul.

The Romans were running around like headless chickens. It was all I could do not to laugh when JC started tearing his hair out.

"My magnificent fleet!" he cried. "It's all gone."

"Oh, my," I said. "So it is!"

I've lost my chance for escape.

The Brits have been attacking anywhere the Romans look weak and retreating as soon as reinforcements show up. I think JC finally realized he had bitten off more than he could chew. So this morning, the orders came to set sail back to Gaul in anything that floats.

This is bad news for me, but good news for the Brits, who lined the shore to see us off. They shouted things like "Don't forget to write," and "Come again soon." They have a lot of nerve.

Northern Gaul

JC nearly went crazy when he saw this morning's paper:

The Gauldian

BRITZ BLITZ JOOLZ!

By our man in Rome, Sandix Gaul

The Roman Senate is reported to be quite furious with Julius Caesar, Proconsul of Gaul, for getting Rome involved in wars in places it's never heard of. Senator Cato argued yesterday that Caesar should be charged with treason.

Pompey went even further, saying sarcastically that if Caesar was determined to fight the Britons, he should have tried not to get beaten so badly.

"All he had to do was defeat the British," Pompey told our reporter. "What's the problem?"

When I went into JC's room this afternoon, I caught him standing in front of his mirror with his nose in the air, roaring, "I shall return!" He turned all red when he saw me, and he gave me a lecture about sneaking up on him.

I didn't mind though. It sounds as if he's going to try to invade Brittania again. Maybe I'll get another chance to escape after all!

JC's not waiting around this time. He put an ad in all the papers:

The Roman merchants couldn't wait to get in on the act and added another 200 ships to JC's fleet. So now JC has 800 ships and five legions for his invasion.

Brittania (again)

What a trip! Gales have blown the Roman fleet right up the English Channel and almost into the North Sea. When we finally dropped anchor, JC came over and said, "Commonus, where are we?"

"Sandwich," I replied.

He said no thanks, he'd just eaten.

I had to explain that Sandwich was a place in Kent.

"What a silly name," he said, and went off to give orders for going ashore.

You'd have thought JC would have learned. Just before he headed out to fight the Brits, I realized he hadn't beached the ships safely again. "You don't want to leave those ships at anchor," I told him. "It's marshy around here, and you know what they say, 'Beware the Tides of Marsh.'"

He threw a fit. Was I, a mere slave, telling him, the General of the Roman Army, how to manage his fleet? Any more lip and I'd be shipped off to the Circus Maximus, etc., etc.

All right, pal, I thought, have it your way. I'm not saying another word.

Sure enough, three days after we landed, while JC was upcountry somewhere chasing Brits, the wind started howling again. Guess what? The storm smashed about half the fleet into matchsticks and severely damaged the rest. It serves JC right. With his invasion fleet in ruins, there's nothing left for him to do but get back here and wait to be rescued.

When am I going to stop underestimating JC? You'd think *I'd* learn.

He broke off the fight with the Britons . . . for all of *eleven days*, while he sent a load of legionnaires back to the beach. They repaired the damaged boats and sent some of them back to Gaul to pick up boatbuilders and more ships. As soon as they'd finished, the soldiers went right back to JC again, ready for some more fighting.

The British papers are trying to sound confident that our men will beat the Romans. I wish *I* was.

News of the Woad

BRITISH Secret Weapon Routs Romans

Summer 54BC   Price: Three Chickens

King Cassivellaunus* unleashed his secret weapon on the invaders yesterday as the Romans were approaching the Thames River. Four thousand war chariots swept down on the legions, causing panic in the Roman ranks. It seems the Romans use chariots only for racing and processions and were totally unprepared for mechanized warfare.

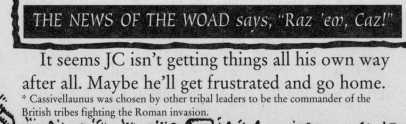

After they struck, the charioteers pulled back, and latest reports suggest they are continuing to mount lightning raids on Roman columns.

Meanwhile, Cassivellaunus is making his camp on the north bank of the river. He has planted stakes on the riverbed as a trap for the Roman cavalry. A spokesman from Cassivellaunus's staff is quoted as saying, "If they don't like it, too bad!"

THE NEWS OF THE WOAD says, "Raz 'em, Caz!"

It seems JC isn't getting things all his own way after all. Maybe he'll get frustrated and go home.

* Cassivellaunus was chosen by other tribal leaders to be the commander of the British tribes fighting the Roman invasion.

News of the Woad

Late Summer 54BC   Price: Three Chickens

Roman Secret Weapon Blasts Brits

The invading Roman army turned the tables on King Cassivellaunus yesterday when a giant animal with a fort on its back sent waves of panic through British forces. As the dreadful beast waded into the river, the defenders dropped their weapons and fled in terror.

King Cassivellaunus is reported to have told the *News,* "We shall fight on the beaches, we shall fight on the landing grounds, we shall fight in the fields and in the streets, we shall fight in the hills; we shall never surren—OH NO! WHAT'S THAT HUGE THING? LE-LEMME OUTTA HERE!"

I know what the secret weapon was. It was an elephant. The Romans brought it in the biggest ship I've ever seen. They said it came from India. It had armor especially made for it, and tusks, and a tail at both ends. I don't blame our men for running away.

Of course, when a thing that size does its business, you don't want to be standing behind it, and guess which slave had to clean up the mess afterward?

Portus Itius, Gaul

In spite of beating Cassivellaunus, JC decided
he couldn't stay in Brittania. Even with the
replacement ships, he never had enough to
supply the army properly. He was a little
nervous about storms and tides anyway, and I
did my part by saying things like "I don't like
the look of that sky" and "Of course, the sea
gets very rough this time of year." Eventually,
JC decided he didn't want to get trapped again,
so we're back in Gaul.

Things aren't great here: JC received a letter
saying that his daughter Julia, who was married
to Pompey, has died. Also, Delus Boyus and
Roddus have been complaining because they
didn't get many slaves
from Brittania, and the
ones they did get are
the bargain-basement
variety. There are
also rumors that the
Belgians may revolt.
It looks like it's
going to be a long,
hard winter.

Lutetia,* Gaul

JC's been a real hairy monster lately.

The reason is, the Belgians rebelled earlier this year. JC swore he wouldn't cut his hair or shave his beard until he got revenge.

He wiped out the Eburone tribe, who'd been responsible for massacring his legions. He also had the leader of a neighboring tribe stripped and bound to a stake, beaten to death until he'd learned his lesson, and beheaded so he wouldn't do it again.

Then he sent out for a barber. I think he looks much better without the mustache.

The **Gauldian**

CRASSUS CRASHES OUT!

By *our man in Rome,* Sandix Gaul

The Triumvirate is today only a Twoumvirate. News has reached Rome of the death of Crassus, who has been killed in battle with King Juba of Numidia.

With gangs of thugs still terrorizing the city and Caesar away, it seems likely that Pompey will emerge as Head Honcho when the dust settles.

LATE NEWS
CLODIUS CLOBBERED!

News just in: the Twoumvirate is now a Oneumvirate. The gangster Clodius was killed last night in a fight with a rival gang. Rioting has broken out in Rome; the Senate House and buildings near the Forum* have been set on fire. As law and order break down, it seems certain that Pompey will be elected sole Consul or possibly even Dictator of Rome to clean up the city.

*A cross between a market and a meeting place; the center of life in Rome

Ravenna, Cisalpina Gaul

JC threw a tantrum as soon as he read the paper today: hysterical outbursts, blue in the face, kicking his legs. Just like a big kid.

"Why is that fat nerd Pompey so popular?" he sobbed. "What's he got that I haven't got? Nobody loves me!"

Since Pompey was elected Consul, JC's been running a Mister Popularity campaign. Although he's not allowed to go to Rome himself, he's had his supporters working on all kinds of stunts. So far, he's:

- had a new Forum built in Rome
- paid for an all-singing, all dancing (well, all-chopping, all-slaying) gladiator show at the Circus Maximus
- doubled his soldiers' pay and given every soldier a Gallic slave
- invited all the bigwigs in Rome up here for a huge party

What a night that was!

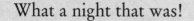

Hundreds of people showed up, lay around on couches, and helped themselves to mountains of food. Some of the guests stuffed so much food and wine into their stomachs that they had to go outside to a vomitorium, make themselves throw up, then come back in and eat some more!

I'm not surprised they wanted to throw up. I felt sick just reading the menu!

BANQUET MENU

APPETIZERS
JELLYFISH AND EGGS
SOWS' UDDERS STUFFED WITH SEA URCHINS
BRAINS COOKED IN MILK AND EGGS
TREE FUNGI
SNAILS FATTENED WITH MILK
OYSTERS AND SEA URCHINS
OLIVES & CHEESE

MAIN COURSE
SELECTION OF ROAST BIRDS, INCLUDING
JACKDAWS, CROWS, RAVENS, AND THRUSHES
WILD BOAR
ROAST DEER
ROAST PEACOCK WITH HONEY SAUCE
BOILED FLAMINGO WITH DATES
GRAPE LEAVES STUFFED WITH PORK AND PINE KERNELS
(SERVED ON A STICK)

VEGETABLES, INCLUDING
NETTLES, DANDELIONS, AND SEAWEED

DESSERT
FRICASSEE OF ROSES
DATES STUFFED WITH NUTS AND HONEY
FRUIT AND NUTS

WINE
RED AND WHITE FROM GREECE AND ROME

Lots of it!

There was entertainment too: dancers, jugglers, and acrobats. The highlight of the evening was when two gladiators were called in to fight. There were blood and guts everywhere! Pukus Uppus lived up to his name—he created a new mosaic on the floor! This caused a chain reaction that ended with nearly everyone standing in the vomitorium getting rid of what they'd put in.

Inkus Fingus got as drunk as a skunk. I tried to warn him; these clerks can get tipsy just standing near an open bottle. He ended up dancing on the table, singing a rude song he had made up about JC . . .

Our General Julius Caesar,
Has an incredible sneezer!
One blast from his nose
Drowns whole armies of foes.
That's why he's a Roman crowd-pleaser.

Everyone laughed and applauded. JC went red in the face.

The night proved that money can't buy you love. JC went to bed feeling pretty unhappy. But he wasn't nearly as unhappy as Inkus will be in the morning when I tell him what he did at the party!

The **Gauldian**
WHAT A GAUL!

The Roman army of occupation is reeling from a widespread uprising in Gaul, led by Chief Vercingetorix of the Arveni.

Roman officials have been put to death at Cenabum.* Caesar is reported to be enraged that Gauls who had promised peace are now rebelling against the Roman Empire. "I've had it!" he told our reporter. "No more Mr. Nice Guy."

- 52 BC -

Ravenna, Cisalpina Gaul

JC's marching out tomorrow (with me in tow, as usual). He's furious. He thought he had conquered Gaul, and now he's got to fight for it all over again. I hope this Vercingetorix character knows what he's doing, because JC is determined to crush this revolt, and I don't think he'll be taking many prisoners.

*Orleans

The **Gauldian**

ALESIA, ALESIA, ALL FALL DOWN!

ALESIA

possible attack from town

Wooden Palisades

possible attack from relief force

Roman Encampment

Today, Vercingetorix and his army of 80,000 are helpless prisoners in their own citadel of Alesia, along with the inhabitants of the town, under siege from Caesar's legions.

The legions have built a double ring of fortifications— the inner circle being 10 miles (16 km) in circumference and the outer, 14 miles (23 km)— around Alesia.

The army is encamped between the trenches and is therefore safe from attack from inside the fort, and from any reinforcements that might try to help Vercingetorix. It is thought that the rebels have food for only about thirty days.

The gates of Alesia were opened, and Chief Vercingetorix sent out everybody who wasn't involved in the fighting: women, kids, and old people. The gates closed behind them.

JC wouldn't let them go, and Vercingetorix wouldn't let them back into the city. So they just wandered around between the city walls and our trenches until they all starved to death.

Vercingetorix's reinforcements eventually arrived, all 250,000 of them!

JC was in the middle of it, fighting alongside his men for four days. When he broke the attack, it was the end of the line for Vercingetorix. JC has decided to keep him in chains and send him back to Rome. The prisoners of war are to be divided up between the soldiers as slaves. (I could see Delus Boyus in the background greedily rubbing his hands together; most of the soldiers will sell their slaves to him.)

But it could have been worse. Since his victory, JC has been acting very generous. The other rebel leaders are to be pardoned, and the people of the tribes who followed Vercingetorix will be allowed to go home.

So, when JC beat Vercingetorix at Alesia, he finally completed his conquest of Gaul. He's sure Pompey will be green with envy when he hears about it.

But I don't believe for a minute JC will be satisfied with being in charge of Gaul. Guys like JC are never satisfied. He'll be after Rome next, take my word for it.

I drew a map of the campaign in Gaul:

Destroyed, along with most of the Inhabitants

Burned by its Inhabitants (the Parisi) to prevent it from falling into Caesar's hands

Lutetia

JC finally chased Big V. and his army into Gaul's greatest fortress

Cenabum

Avaricum   **Noviodunum**

Alesia

Destroyed with all its inhabitants (40,000)—not a single person got out alive

Gergovia

Rebelled while JC was attacking Gergovia and massacred Roman garrison

Attacked by JC but proved too strong—hundreds of legionnaires and 46 Centurions killed

Ravenna, Cisalpina Gaul

I had a talk with Inkus Fingus today. I haven't seen him for a while: He's been busy copying over his notes on the wars in Gaul. When JC's not generaling, he spends most of his time dictating his memoirs, which means getting Inkus to write about how clever JC was at the Battle of Whatsit or the Siege of Such-and-such. For some reason, JC doesn't say "I did this" and "I did that," he always says "Caesar did this" and "Caesar did that," as if he's talking about somebody else.

Inkus says it's propaganda. I call it showing off.

- 50 BC -

Ravenna, Cisalpina Gaul

It's been a quiet year. Inkus has been recording exactly what JC's done over the past few years. It's pretty impressive:

- fought against 8 million men
- captured 800 towns
- conquered 200,000 square miles (322 sq. km) of territory.

Inkus says no Roman leader has ever done this much. What's more, the Roman slave markets are full of Gauls, the banks are bulging with Caesar's money, and his books on the Gallic Wars are selling like hotcakes.

Still, I wouldn't want to be in JC's sandals for all the olive oil in Rome. He's not well; he has funny spells* occasionally, and he's not sleeping soundly. Guilty conscience, I guess.

*Caesar suffered from epilepsy.

The **Gauldian**

AN ENEMY OF THE PEOPLE?

By our man in Rome, Sandix Gaul

The Senate today took steps to protect Rome against Julius Caesar, Proconsul of Gaul. Caesar has grown so powerful that Pompey has been authorized to raise an army in case Caesar should choose to march on Rome.

The Senate's fears were fueled by the news that Caesar has been secretly moving his legions to Cisalpina Gaul, just across the frontier. Messengers have been sent to demand that Caesar disband his army at once or be declared an enemy of Rome.

Ravenna, Cisalpina Gaul

Messengers have been going in and out of JC's
headquarters for days now. I wondered what was
going on until I saw the paper this morning. Inkus
Fingus says that while the Triumvirate was in
charge, the Senate couldn't do anything about JC.
Now there's only Pompey left, and since he and
JC have quarreled, the Senate can act. If the Senate
decides to recall JC from his post as Proconsul of
Gaul, he'll have only two choices:

1 To obey the Senate, go back to Rome, and get murdered... OR

2 to fight!

If I know JC, he'll fight.

I was just putting the cat out tonight when a
slave showed up and asked to see Caesar. I told him
to go to the servants' entrance around the back. I didn't
like the looks of him: His clothes were covered with
dirt, and he smelled like a goat. I said JC wasn't
seeing anybody.

"He'll see me," the slave insisted, and he pushed past me.

I yelled for the guards, but I shouldn't have bothered. It turned out that the "slave" was Mark Antony, JC's spy in the Senate. He's been keeping an eye on JC's affairs in Rome while JC's been in Gaul. JC's name has been mud since the Senate came out against him, and Mark Antony had to disguise himself as a slave to get away from Rome before he got a dagger in the back.

Inkus Fingus says Mark Antony is a two-faced creep. "Watch out for him," Inkus said. "He has eyes everywhere."

"Gotcha," I said. "Beware the eyes of Mark."

The Rubicon River*

JC ordered his legions in Gaul to march south.
We'd been marching for hours this morning
when we came to a little river and everybody
stopped. The troops took up defensive positions
while JC went into a huddle with the other
officers. Of course, nobody bothered to tell me
what was going on, and I got bored. There was
no enemy in sight, so I took my sandals off and
went for a swim.

There was a lot of shouting and waving from
the legionnaires on the bridge, but I
thought they were just fooling around
so I waved back. Then JC appeared
and yelled, "Commonus Muccus,
get out of there *at once*."

*This river is now called the Fiumicino.

Well, always willing to oblige, I paddled over to the nearest shore (which happened to be on the other side of the river from JC and the legions) and turned around to see what he wanted.

JC stared at me for a moment, then yelled, "The die is cast!" and ordered his men across the river.

Inkus Fingus came over, holding my sandals. "You know what you've done, don't you?"

I said I didn't.

"Roman law says that no general is allowed to take his soldiers out of their own province without permission from the Senate. Well, this little river is the boundary between Cisalpina Gaul on one side and Rome on the other. You're in JC's army and you've just crossed it. You've just forced Caesar to declare war on Rome."

"Oops," I said.

Ariminum[*]

I think JC would have crossed the Rubicon anyway. It was either that or give up his army, and JC would never do that.

The trouble is, it's not much of an army; only one legion. JC's assessing the situation, pointing out that:

- Pompey hasn't seen active service for more than twelve years
- He's in his fifties now
- He's been seriously ill recently
- The only troops he actually has under his command are raw recruits and retired veterans
- The Roman legions will come over to our side as soon as Caesar asks them to.

I asked him why the legions would join us. He drew himself up and looked down his nose again. "I will win them over with a brilliant speech, the way I always do."

Well, JC was right. He told the troops that Pompey was a traitor. I don't know whether they believed him or if they just preferred having JC lead them rather than Pompey. Anyway, they all decided to join JC.

The Daily Espresso

SENATORS SCRAM!

Julius Caesar's army continues on its triumphal march south. City after city has opened its gates and offered no resistance to the invading army. On hearing of the advance, most of the Senators have fled from Rome. Pompey has set sail for Macedonia* rather than risk battle, and Rome now stands at Caesar's mercy. The few Senators left in the city have asked Caesar to be Dictator in a bid to save Rome from disaster.

INSIDE: THE MARTHA STEWARTUS RECIPE: CAESAR SALAD (PAGE XI)

*Greece

It looks as though JC will be able to walk into Rome any time he likes. Good news—a weekend off would suit me just fine, and I've heard a lot about Rome. I've got plans for a weekend of nonstop sports with a little of the old nightlife thrown in. I bought myself a trendy new toga to wear barhopping, so those Roman girls had better watch out!

Brundisium*

It doesn't look as though I'm going to get to Rome, after all. JC knows he can't march into Rome until he beats Pompey, so we're going to have to follow him. JC's gathering his legions at the harbor while he assembles a fleet to sail across to Macedonia.

A funny thing happened on the way here, but not funny ha ha. The Ninth Legion mutinied when it found out that all of Pompey's legions that had surrendered were being allowed to go home, while JC's legions had to keep fighting.

* Brindisi

JC called the officers to assemble the legion, and he told them that the punishment for mutiny was decimation. One man in every ten would be chosen by lot and killed.

The legionnaires all started weeping and wailing. The officers fell to their knees and begged JC to let them off, promising that they would never mutiny again.

In the end, JC agreed that if 120 of the ringleaders were handed over for punishment, he'd forget the whole thing. Twelve of those handed over would be put to death.

The twelve were chosen by lot. That's what I call dicing with death.

Dear In...

Here we are in ...
really like eating things with te...
it was awful, too, because they all smash...
danced on them.

Anyway, I hope you're enjoying Rome (you lucky guy), even if you do
have to spend most of your time writing up notes for JC's new book on
the Civil War.

I'm sending you a postcard of the place we landed, only you can't
see us landing because the picture was taken before we got there. The
crossing was terrible, cold and really rough, but at least we were able
to land before Pompey found out we were here.

We're off to fight Pompey tomorrow—hooray! JC says it'll all be
over by Saturnalia.

Best wishes,
Commonus Muccus

Apollonia, Macedonia

Inkus Fingus,
c/o The Caesars,
Ididitmy Way,
Rome

Dear Inkus,

Here we are in Greece. Went to a restaurant last night. I don't
really like eating things with tentacles. Everyone else must have thought
it was awful, too, because they all smashed their plates on the floor and
danced on them.

Anyway, I hope you're enjoying Rome (you lucky guy), even if you do
have to spend most of your time writing up notes for JC's new book on
the Civil War.

I'm sending you a postcard of the place we landed, only you can't
see us landing because the picture was taken before we got there. The
crossing was terrible, cold and really rough, but at least we were able
to land before Pompey found out we were here.

We're off to fight Pompey tomorrow—hooray! JC says it'll all be
over by Saturnalia.

Best wishes,
Commonus Muccus

JC nearly lost it today. Pompey still has more men than he does, and when they attacked, JC lost 1,000 men and 32 standards, or banners. The legions are very proud of their standards, which they carry into battle, so this was a bad blow.

JC wasn't going to curl up and die though. He made a speech to the men. He reminded them of all the battles they had fought and won together, and then he had the 32 bearers who had abandoned their standards demoted (not executed; he must be getting softhearted).

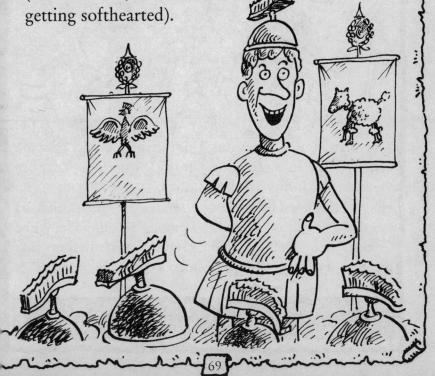

ROME'S FAVORITE NEWSPAPER

The Daily Espresso

June 6, 48 BC

FROM OUR CORRESPONDENT IN MACEDONIA

POMPEY IS A PUSHOVER

The battle of Pharsalus ended today in a stunning victory for Julius Caesar. His forces routed Pompey's cavalry and started a panic. Caesar then declared that the war between Romans was over and from now on his army would pursue only Pompey's foreign allies.

Fifteen thousand of Pompey's followers were killed, and thousands more surrendered. Caesar lost 200 men.

INSIDE: RICHES TO RAGS—POMPEY'S OWN HEARTBREAKING STORY, TOLD EXCLUSIVELY TO THE ESPRESSO.

The Hellespont*

Word came a few days ago that Pompey had set sail for Egypt, so of course JC was dying to go after him.

The trouble was, his warships weren't ready. He wouldn't wait, so that's why we were caught crossing the Hellespont like sitting ducks in an unarmed transport ship when half of Pompey's fleet showed up armed to the teeth.

Well, there was only one sensible thing to do, and I did it. While I was lying in the bottom of the boat whimpering, JC climbed up to the front end of the boat. He demanded that Pompey's ten heavily armed warships surrender to him in his tiny little boat. Oh, ha ha, in your dreams, I thought bitterly.

But they did.

* The Dardanelles strait that separates Asia from Europe

Troy

JC has decided he's in no rush to follow Pompey to Egypt after all. He's playing tourist. He came here because he figures that Aeneas, who got away when Troy was destroyed by the Greeks and then sailed to Italy and founded Rome, is an ancestor of his.

"Really?" I said. "Imagine that."

"And what's more," he went on, gazing lovingly at his reflection in a store window, "Aeneas's mother was the goddess Venus, so I myself am descended from the gods."

I think my boss's head is getting as large as his nose.

My Little Wooden Horsey

The Daily Espresso

PTOLEMY PTOPS POMPEY!

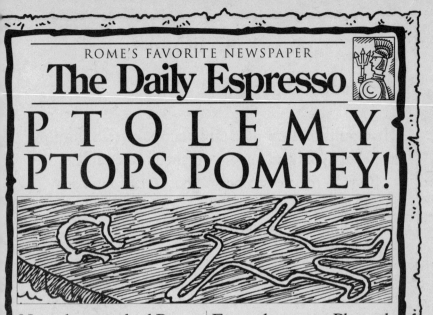

News has reached Rome that Pompey, Caesar's archrival for control of the Roman government, has been *murdered* in Egypt.

When Pompey fled from Caesar's forces and sought refuge in Alexandria, he was unaware that civil war had broken out in Egypt between Pharaoh Ptolemy XIII and his lovely sister, Cleopatra. Eyewitness reports say that as Pompey stepped ashore, he was stabbed in the back. Pompey drew his robe over his head and fell, dying.

On Ptolemy's orders, Pompey's severed head was taken to Caesar.

Alexandria, Egypt

"It would make a nice table lamp," I said, looking at Pompey's head sitting on the coffee table.

JC told me not to be so gross. (But later I noticed him holding a couple of lampshades over Pompey's head, looking at them and saying "Hmmmm . . .")

As soon as the messenger showed up with Pompey's head, JC set sail for Egypt to have a talk with Ptolemy. After all, Egypt is supposed to be an ally of Rome, and you can't have allies bumping off one of your top generals, even if he is your enemy.

I can see why Ptolemy had to get rid of Pompey. His arrival had put Ptolemy in a tight spot:

• If Ptolemy helped Pompey, he would offend Caesar.

• If he refused to help, Pompey might join forces with Cleopatra.

I asked JC why Ptolemy and Cleopatra were fighting anyway. I'd heard they were brother and sister. JC said yes, they were, and they were also married.

"Wait a minute," I said. "Isn't that illegal?"

JC said not for Egyptian royals. In fact, it was compulsory, and didn't I have any work to do, because if I didn't he could find me some.

Imagine being married to your sister! I wouldn't want to be married to mine, that's for sure.

I had just picked up JC's toga from the cleaners when a messenger arrived to say the carpet had come.

Well, I hadn't ordered a carpet, but waste not want not, I always say, so I told him to bring it in.

He brought it in all rolled up, and JC and I watched as he unrolled it.

A young lady fell out of the end of the carpet and landed at Caesar's feet. It figures, I thought. The last time *I* bought a carpet all I got was 10 percent off.

JC's eyes nearly popped out. "Stunning," he said. "Beautiful. Absolutely gorgeous."

"Yes, very nice," I said. "One hundred percent wool, isn't it?"

He glared at me. "Not the carpet, you fool!" He helped the young woman up and asked her who she was.

She drew herself up proudly and said, "We are Cleopatra, Queen of Egypt."

JC has been following Cleopatra around all day like a lovesick schoolboy. It's pathetic—he's old enough to be her father!

It's not just that he likes her. She came here to warn JC that Ptolemy was bringing his army to Alexandria to kick him out. She came to JC's palace hidden in the carpet so she wouldn't be captured by Ptolemy's guards.

Ptolemy himself showed up the day after she did, and you should have seen his face when he saw her sitting next to JC. He blew his top, threw his crown on the floor, and jumped up and down on it, howling that he'd been betrayed. "Ptricked!" he cried. "Oh, ptreason!"

Then he lost his ptemper and threw a ptantrum.

Ptolemy's army has pturned up, and we are in big ptrouble.

The situation is this:

- JC has Ptolemy locked up
- Cleopatra is now JC's girlfriend as well as his ally
- The citizens of Alexandria are rioting outside the palace
- The Egyptian army (which outnumbers JC's guard by about 5 to 1) has arrived and is laying siege to the palace
- Arsinoë, Cleopatra and Ptolemy's younger sister, has escaped to lead the uprising against us.

And, just to make the circumstances even more desperate, I can't get a decent cappuccino anywhere in Alexandria.

JC did something today that embarrassed even him.

The Egyptian fleet had been blockading the harbor to stop Roman reinforcements from getting in. So JC, brazen as ever, took a few of his men and set fire to the Egyptian ships.

The problem was, the fire from the ships spread to the docks, and the Library of Alexandria went up in flames. JC was horrified (well, he's a writer himself). It seems this was the most famous library in the world, full of the greatest books by the most brilliant writers in history. All irreplaceable. The whole of human knowledge was going up in smoke before our very eyes.

"Yes, but look on the bright side," I said. "Aren't the flames pretty?"

I was delighted. I had an overdue book from the library, and now I won't have to pay the fine.

QUIET PLEASE

I could strangle JC.

He came in today soaking wet and dripped water all over my clean floor. I said, "You look like a drowned rat."

I found out later he'd been taking another shot at the Egyptian navy. He sank a couple of their ships, then got a bit too cocky and tried to capture the Pharos—that's the lighthouse at the entrance to the harbor. The Egyptians cut him off, and he and his men had to escape in small boats. About 400 men were drowned when their boats overturned, and JC had to swim for it. He even had to leave his cloak behind.

So now he's gone to bed with Teddus and a temperature. He's got to stop playing these childish games—I'm getting tired of cleaning up after him!

I delivered a message to JC yesterday. It was written on a dirty bit of papyrus, and it said:

Dere Seezar.
Plese may we hav owr
King bak?
Yors faythfuly
The EgypshunArmy

JC said, "Fine. If they want him they can have him."

I said, "But won't Ptolemy raise an army against you?"

JC put on his long-suffering look and spoke to me as though I were a three-year-old. He told me that:

1. Ptolemy is a useless ptwit

2. His sister Arsinoë is giving the army its orders now, but she's very unpopular

3. So if he gave Ptolemy back, the army would take orders from him instead, and because he's so useless, the army would be a mess.

"If Ptolemy decides to fight," JC said, "I'll wipe out his army, and if he decides to run away, the Egyptian army will kill him. Either way, Ptolemy pturns his ptoes up and leaves Cleopatra in charge."

"And you, of course," I added.

They've got some big newts called crocodiles in the rivers here, and I thought they could smile, but the grin that JC gave just then beat them all!

JC called Ptolemy in today and said he was sending him back to his people.

Ptolemy burst into ptears (he's obviously not as stupid as he looks) and begged to stay with Caesar, but JC said no. So Ptolemy ptoddled off without even waving pta pta.

The Daily Espresso

CAESAR ROCKS MEMPHIS!

Long-distance reports from Memphis bring the news that Caesar's army has wiped out the Egyptian forces in a two-day battle. The Egyptian king, Ptolemy, was killed in the battle, which leaves Cleopatra as sole ruler of Egypt.

INSIDE: SECRETS OF ETERNAL BEAUTY FROM CLEOPATRA, QUEEN OF EGYPT.
PART ONE: THE C-PLAN DIET.

Cleo looked a little upset this morning. Uh-oh, something's going on, I thought. So when she went in to see JC, I listened to the conversation through the keyhole. It went like this:

Well, can you blame me?

JC just got back after putting down a rebellion in Asia Minor. I asked him how it went.

"Veni, Vidi, Vici," he said. "I came, I saw, I conquered."

Well, pardon me for asking. What a big head! If you want to know what I think, JC's starting to love himself way too much.

Rome

At last, here I am in Rome. What a place!

I never imagined anywhere could be so big! (Or so crowded, noisy, dirty, and smelly!)

It's an amazing city. I've been doing some sightseeing. They've got these open-topped carts with names like "The Rome Experience," and they take you to all the famous sights: the Circus Maximus, the Forum, the Theater of Pompey, and the Temple of Jupiter, to name a few.

Everything is so modern here. I'll give you an example: At home, when we want water, we get it from the river. Here, they've built a great stone channel called an aqueduct to bring the river into the city!

Rich people live in mansions and villas that make the biggest palace in Brittania look like a cowshed. Poorer people live in strange houses piled on top of each other, with lots of families all living in one building. They call these places insulae. I don't know how Romans live in them—it must be like living in a henhouse. Inkus Fingus says the rent is astronomical.

There's lots to do and see in Rome.

Me at the baths.
People spend hours in these baths talking, exercising, and even washing.

A day at the races—I lost a bundle!

They even have places for kids to learn things. They call them schools!

CIRCUS MAXIMUS

They've got the World Gladiator Championships at the Circus Maximus next week, and JC gave me a ticket! (Well, actually, I stole it off his desk.) Come on, you Gladdies!

ITALIA 50!
WORLD CUP GLADIATORS
VENUE: CIRCUS MAXIMUS, ROME

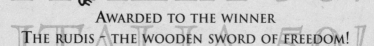

AWARDED TO THE WINNER
THE RUDIS – THE WOODEN SWORD OF FREEDOM!

YOUR GUIDE TO THE ITALIA 50! WITH BOBUS COSTUS

WELCOME TO THE ITALIA 50. GLAD YOU CAN BE HERE. IT'S GOING TO BE THUMBS DOWN FOR THE LOSERS AND ROARS OF "IUGULA!"* VERY FEW PEOPLE ARE EXPECTING TO HEAR "MISSOS"** OR "MITTE."*** THIS YEAR IT'S A FIGHT TO THE DEATH, AND THE WINNER TAKES ALL!

THERE SHOULD BE SOME GREAT CONTESTS IN THE ARENA. IT'S ALL ABOUT STYLES. CONTINENTAL TACTICS SHOULD PROVE TOO MUCH FOR THE GLADIATORS FROM AFRICA AND BRITTANIA. THE DIFFERENT STYLES OF FIGHTING SHOULD MAKE IT AN EXCITING BATTLE FOR EVERYONE. IT'S GOING TO BE SWIFT AND NIMBLE VERSUS SLOW AND HEAVY.

* cut his throat ** let him go *** stop the fight (spare him)

THE STYLES

THE RETARIUS
THE RETARIUS IS ARMED WITH ONLY A TRIDENT AND A NET. THIS STYLE DEPENDS ON SPEED IN ORDER TO NET THE OPPONENT BEFORE A QUICK STAB.

THE MYRMILLO
THIS GLADIATOR IS HEAVILY ARMED AND PROTECTED. LOTS OF ARMOR MAKES HIM SLOW—BUT DEADLY!

THE THRACIAN
THE THRACIAN HAS A SMALL CURVED DAGGER AND BUCKLER* AND A VISORED HELMET. SPEED AND AGILITY ARE REQUIRED.

THE SAMNITE
SIMILAR TO THE MYRMILLO, THE SAMNITE IS HEAVILY ARMED AND CARRIES A SWORD AND SHIELD.

* a small round shield

MEET THE GLADIATORS

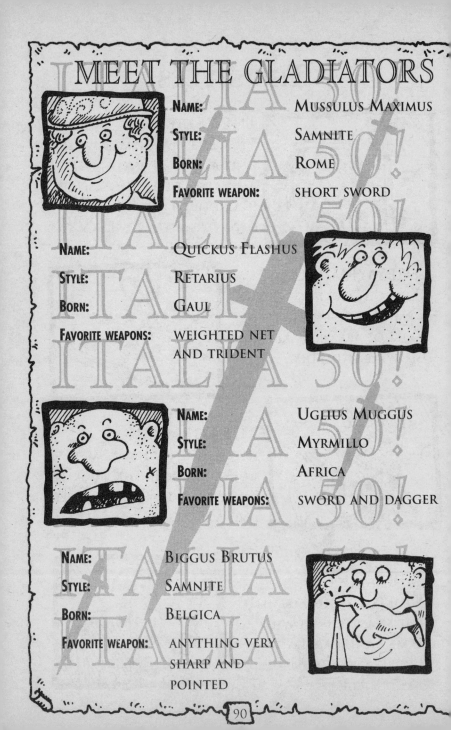

NAME: MUSSULUS MAXIMUS

STYLE: SAMNITE

BORN: ROME

FAVORITE WEAPON: SHORT SWORD

NAME: QUICKUS FLASHUS

STYLE: RETARIUS

BORN: GAUL

FAVORITE WEAPONS: WEIGHTED NET AND TRIDENT

NAME: UGLIUS MUGGUS

STYLE: MYRMILLO

BORN: AFRICA

FAVORITE WEAPONS: SWORD AND DAGGER

NAME: BIGGUS BRUTUS

STYLE: SAMNITE

BORN: BELGICA

FAVORITE WEAPON: ANYTHING VERY SHARP AND POINTED

NAME:	JOCKUS McPICT
STYLE:	RETARIUS
BORN:	BRITTANIA
FAVORITE WEAPON:	BROKEN BOTTLE

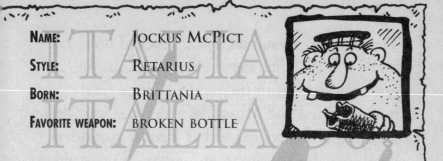

NAME:	COWARDUS CUSTURDUS
STYLE:	CHICKEN
BORN:	SICILLIA
FAVORITE WEAPON:	SHIELD (A VERY BIG ONE)
FAVORITE TACTIC:	RUNNING AWAY AS QUICKLY AS POSSIBLE

NAME:	SHARPUS POINTUS
STYLE:	THRACIAN
BORN:	HISPANIA
FAVORITE WEAPON:	SHORT CURLED DAGGER (VERY SHARP!)

NAME:	HED SHOLDERSNEESUNTOES
STYLE:	MYRMILLO
BORN:	GERMANIA
FAVORITE WEAPON:	LONG SWORD (THE LONGER THE BETTER)

The Italia 50 wasn't all it was cracked up to be. Some of the fights were very good, but McPict got knocked out in the semis, and the final between Hed and Mussulus was a washout. It was a boring defensive draw that went to a sudden-death penalty shootout, and when I say "sudden death" I'm not kidding. Hed won, if anybody's interested.

Anyway, it's back to work today. The army mutinied again. They found out they're going to be sent to take care of Pompey's supporters in Africa, and they aren't thrilled with the idea.

JC went to listen to their complaints. I don't mind telling you, I was petrified. Thousands of hardened soldiers, tough as old boots and really ticked off—they could have torn us to shreds. I don't think that ever occurred to JC.

They told him they were disgusted. They wanted to leave the army and collect the pay and land they had been promised. This is what happened next, and if you don't believe it, well, I don't believe it either, and I was there.

In the end, JC agreed to keep them all. How does he do it? Don't ask me, I'm only a slave.
* See page 67 on mutiny and decimation

The Daily Espresso

TROOPS TO SAIL FOR AFRICA

Caesar has resigned the Dictatorship in order to sail to Africa, where Pompey's last remaining supporters have gathered. These include Pompey's sons, Gnaeus and Sextus, and:

- Caesar's old chief of staff, Labienus
- Generals Afrianus and Scipio
- Caesar's old political enemy Senator Cato
- King Juba of Numidia (who ended the Triumvirate by killing Crassus)

Caesar was in a confident mood as he supervised the embarkation of his six legions, but his position is not good. Enemy forces are reported to consist of:

- 14 legions
- 15,000 cavalry
- 100 elephants

Though he's heavily outnumbered, Caesar is still determined to set sail for Africa and to do it as quickly as possible.

INSIDE: WOMEN'S PAGE—YOUR COMPLEXION: IS BATHING IN GOAT'S MILK OR DONKEY'S MILK BETTER FOR YOUR SKIN?

Africa

Just before we landed, I noticed a strap on JC's sandals was loose, so I bent down to fix it.

He turned around and glared at me. "Oh, stop fussing, Commonus!"

Please yourself, you old grouch, I thought, but if you trip on that and fall flat on your face, don't come crying to me.

Sure enough, no sooner had he stepped off the ship than he tripped over his own sandals and went flying. He tried to cover it up by jumping to his feet with a handful of earth and calling out, "I hold Africa in my hand!" He certainly had a fair amount of Africa up his nose.

Inkus Fingus,
c/o The Caesars,
Ididitmy Way
Rome

AFRICA

Dear Inkus,

JC's a little under the weather. I'm not surprised. It's brutally hot here!

You know how he has funny spells sometimes? Well, he had one just before he went into battle against Scipio. It didn't matter because the Roman army was aching for a fight. They used slings and arrows to drive Scipio's elephants mad, and the elephants went trampling through their own lines doing untold damage. The opposition started to panic and tried to surrender, but our boys just chopped them to pieces—along with a few unpopular senators from their own side!

So the war in Africa is over. JC had Afranus executed; King Juba, Cato, and Scipio committed suicide. The only bad news is that Pompey's sons and Labienus have escaped to Hispania*, so there'll probably be more trouble from them. We set sail for Rome tomorrow. I hear there'll be a little party when we get there.

Best wishes,
Commonus Muccus

* Spain

96

Rome

Party is right! They're giving JC a *forty-day* Triumph and making him Dictator for ten years. They've put up a statue of him in the Capitol. Of course, he always thought he was a god—the difference now is that everybody believes him.

JC had visitors today, a couple of men carrying briefcases and wearing hair oil and seriously sharp togas. It turned out they were his new public relations men, Saatchus and Saatchus.

They showed him their plans for his Triumph. It's actually four Triumphs rolled into one, celebrating JC's victories in Gaul, Egypt, Africa, and Asia.

When they left, I sneaked a look at the program. It sounds like a wild time.

INVITATION

TO ALL ROMAN CITIZENS
FROM GAIUS JULIUS CAESAR, DICTATOR OF ROME

I WILL BE HAVING A TRIUMPH THROUGH THE STREETS
OF ROME. I HOPE YOU CAN COME.

PROGRAM:

ORDER OF PROCESSION IN THE TRIUMPH OF GAIUS JULIUS CAESAR, DICTATOR OF ROME

1. A statue of the Ocean in Chains, symbolizing the Conquest of Brittania
2. The Gaul Vercingetorix in chains
3. Queen Cleopatra of Egypt, her son Caesarion, and her sister Arsinoë, a captive
4. Elephants, Cameleopards*, and other exotic beasts
5. A tableau representing the suicides of the traitors Scipio and Cato
6. White Oxen with gilded horns, to be sacrificed at the Capitol
7. Musicians and incense-burners
8. Parade of Lictors with Fasces**
9. The Dictator Gaius Julius Caesar in his Triumphal Chariot

PLUS!

MARCH OF THE RETURNING LEGIONS
DISPLAYS OF PLUNDER FROM THE WARS
FREE WINE IN THE PUBLIC FOUNTAINS
FEASTING AND MERRYMAKING
CITIZENS' RAFFLE

FOLLOWED BY:

GAMES IN THE CIRCUS MAXIMUS!
GLADIATORS
WILD BEAST HUNTS
CHARIOT RACES

COMMUNITY SING-ALONG WITH

GARTHUS BROOKUS

Promoters: Saatchus and Saatchus   *RSVP*

* Giraffes - the first time they had been seen in Rome
**A symbol of Roman power, a bundle of rods, from which we get the word "Fascist"

Later on, Saatchus (or it might have been Saatchus) sent for me and told me I was going to be in the procession.

I'll bet they do. If JC's head gets any bigger, we'll have to widen the doorways.

Well, JC wasn't entirely pleased by what happened at his Triumph.

There were cheering crowds all over the place, of course, and it was a very impressive procession, but the scene of Scipio and Cato killing themselves was a little disappointing. A lot of people booed when it went past, because they felt sorry for JC's enemies.

JC wasn't at the back of the procession. Behind him came the legionnaires, singing a song they'd made up. I watched the back of JC's neck go red when he heard it. Wonderful!

The legions sang:

Home from his triumphal slaughters
Caesar comes: tell your sons and daughters!
When Julius has finished warring,
Things are never, ever boring!

I stood in the back of the chariot holding the crown (my arms were killing me!) and saying, "Remember, Caesar, thou art mortal."

After about the hundredth time, JC said, "Commonus, can we talk?"

"Remember, Caesar, thou art mortal."

"Commonus, if you say that once more, I'll have your intestines fed to the lions while you watch."

Oooh! Sensitive!

We had just reached the Temple of Fortune when the axle broke on our chariot and JC fell out, with me on top of him. Another chariot was brought up, but the crowd started to mutter about bad luck and ill omens. They shut right up when they saw the spread, though. At JC's feast there were 22,000 tables for 200,000 guests, with a party favor and funny hat for everybody.

Saatchus and Saatchus organized JC's show at the Circus Maximus. I kept one of the posters as a souvenir.

WEEKEND GAMES AT THE
CIRCUS MAXIMUS
IN HONOR OF JULIUS CAESAR

GLADIATORIAL COMBATS:
GALLIC PRISONERS vs. EGYPTIAN PRISONERS

WINNERS TO MEET AFRICAN PRISONERS IN THE FINAL

WILD BEAST HUNTS
LIONS vs. SLAVES

TROYUS AIKUS SAYS,

"THE SLAVES HAVE BEEN TRAINING HARD, BUT I'D STILL BACK THE LIONS."

ATHLETICS

JAVELIN THROWING, RUNNING, WRESTLING, AND BEACH VOLLEYBALL

BATTLE BETWEEN TWO ARMIES

500 ON EACH SIDE, WITH ELEPHANTS!

NAVAL SPECTACULAR

THE FLEETS OF EGYPT AND TYRE FIGHT IT OUT IN THE FLOODED ARENA!

They had to include the naval spectacular at the last minute, because the arena flooded when some idiot left the water running.

Guess who? Oops!

Well, thank goodness it's all over. They hauled the last cartload of bodies out of the Circus Maximus this morning. They ought to put a warning on the posters: "Forty-day Triumphs can seriously damage your health." I'm exhausted, and JC has gone to bed with a headache.

It was a good Triumph, but I don't think it made JC as popular as he had hoped. A lot of people are starting to mutter again that JC is setting himself up as a king.

We had a little trouble with JC's wife, Calphurnia, today. I can't blame her for being upset. She has been married to JC for years, but they've never had a son, and now he spends all his time with Cleopatra. Today, Calphurnia came in holding a knife in one hand and Teddus in the other.

"Stop seeing that woman," she snarled, "or the bear gets it."

We managed to rescue Teddus, but she's got a point. The gossip among the slaves is that JC wants to divorce Calphurnia and marry Cleo, so that when he's made King of Rome he'll have an heir to the throne.

JC is losing it! He's gone bonkers!

Not only does he believe he can change the world, now he thinks he can change time!

Back home we have spring, summer, autumn, and winter. Romans have calendars. The Roman calendar has twelve months:

JANUARY
(after Janus, the two-faced god of
secondhand-chariot salesmen)

FEBRUARY
(after Februa, a religious festival involving beating statues
with animal skins. I suppose it passes the time.)

MARCH
(after the god of war, Mars)

APRIL
(from aperire—to open, which is what plant
buds do in the spring)

MAY
(from Maia, the goddess of growth)

JUNE
(in honor of the goddess Juno, wife of Jupiter)

QUINTILIS*
(because it's the fifth month from the start of the
old new year, which used to be on March 1st)

SEXTILIS**
(because it's the sixth month)

SEPTEMBER
(because it's the seventh month)

OCTOBER
(because it's the eighth month)

NOVEMBER
(because it's the ninth month)

DECEMBER
(because it's the tenth month)

---

* This later became July in honor of Julius Caesar.
** This later became August in honor of the Emperor Augustus.

Each month has 29 ½ days, making a year of 354 days; but a year is really 365 ¼ days, so every so often they have to stick an extra month in. During the Civil War against Pompey, they forgot, so JC has decided that this year we have to have three extra months, so 46 BC will have 442 ½ days. Nearly ninety extra days of washing JC's undies! Yuck!

What's more, he's decided that from now on, the year will be 365 days long, and every fourth year they'll put an extra day in, making it a leap year.

I asked the local astrologer, Mysta Mega, to explain this date thing to me. "Well," she said, "we Romans divide the month up into three parts. The Kalends, the Nones, and the Ides. Do you follow me?"

I nodded slowly.

"Now then," she rattled on, "the Kalends always fall on the first of each month. The Nones fall on the 7th in March, May, Quintilis, and October, but on the 5th in all the other months. The Ides fall on the 15th in March, May, Quintilis, and October, but on the 13th in all the rest. And February has a special system that . . ."

At that point I stopped her because my head was aching.

Later on, I saw Caesar looking happily at his new calendar. "People will be using my calendar in two thousand years," he said (dream on!). "I wonder if people will name a month after me?"

I looked at him. Oh, come on, get real, I thought. And if they did, what would they call it?

Julie?

I asked Inkus Fingus why there were so many temples in Rome. I wish I hadn't bothered. Now Inkus is telling me all about the Roman gods. There are hundreds of them!

Roman Gods and Goddesses

Jupiter: the father of the gods

Juno: his wife

Mars: the god of war and chocolate snacks

Venus: the goddess of love

Apollo: god of the Sun and bingo

Diana: the goddess of the Moon

Sprintus: the god of telephones

Walmarta: the goddess of shopping

Pizza: the goddess of TV dinners

Cola: the goddess of soft drinks

Cupid: the god of dating agencies

Ikea: the goddess of flat-pack kitchens

Parkay: the goddess of margarine

Terminus: the god of bus stations

Visa: the goddess of credit cards

Rome

JC is away on business again, taking care of Pompey's sons, who ran away to Hispania. I've had enough war, so I told him I had pneumonia and he let me stay home. He seems to have done okay, if you can believe what you read in the paper.

ROME'S FAVORITE NEWSPAPER

The Daily Espresso

CIVIL WAR FINALLY ENDS!

Reports from the bloodiest battle of the Civil War at Munda in Spain indicate complete victory for Caesar.

The Spanish campaign has been brutal. Both sides have executed prisoners on the spot. At Munda, the savage hand-to-hand combat sickened even hardened veterans. Brother fought against brother as at least 30,000 Romans were killed, including Caesar's former lieutenant and bitter enemy, Labienus. Pompey's son Gnaeus escaped.

LATE NEWS: Reports just in say that Gnaeus has been captured and his severed head sent to Caesar.

INSIDE: FREE FULL-COLOR VC (VICTORY FOR CAESAR) SOUVENIR ISSUE.

JC just got back from Spain, along with his adopted son, Octavius (who's seventeen, all arrogance and acne), and Mark Antony, who joined them on the way back.

JC's nephew Brutus came by today. The minute I saw him, I said to myself, "Here's a fellow who's up to no good." Brutus was buttering JC up so much, I thought I was going to be sick. Anyone else would have smelled a rat, but JC's too full of himself these days to notice.

I told Inkus that if I was JC, I'd steer clear of a guy who:

- Had fought on Pompey's side against JC at Pharsalus
- Was married to Portia, who is Cato's daughter and used to be married to Pompey's admiral, Bibulus
- Was a descendant of Junius Brutus, who got rid of the last King of Rome.

Inkus said the war was over and JC had forgiven Brutus. Well, it's no skin off my nose, but I think JC's going to forgive somebody once too often one of these days.

The Senate has announced it's going to give JC a fifty-day Triumph for Munda. Not only that:

- JC gets to wear his triumphal honors all the time, not just during his Triumph
- They've had a statue of JC erected with the inscription "To the invincible god"
- Statues of JC will be put in every temple in the Republic
- All the anniversaries of JC's victories are to be celebrated every year
- They've made JC Dictator for Life.

All this is very nice, but I don't like the way JC looks. His funny spells are getting worse, and he has terrible nightmares. He's cuddled all the fur off Teddus. He's fifty-five now, and all those years of hard soldiering are catching up with him. Inkus Fingus says that Caesar told the Senate the other day, "I have lived long enough."

JC's completely drunk with power. He thinks he can do anything:

- He has ordered his head to be stamped on coins. Nobody has ever done that before.
- He has started to wear red boots like the ancient kings used to do. Not only does this make him unpopular, but he looks like a complete idiot.

A lot of people think he's going to declare himself Emperor soon, and the Senate won't like that one little bit.

I think I ought to plan an escape route.

JC has had Saatchus and Saatchus working overtime to get the people to accept him as king. No dice.

At the Feast of Lupercal, Mark Antony offered JC the crown of the god Pan, but the crowd booed so much that JC had to refuse it and put it on the head of the statue of Jupiter instead. The people are getting really angry with JC. It'll end badly, take my word for it.

ROME'S FAVORITE NEWSPAPER

The Daily Espresso

CAESAR TO BE KING!

The Dictator of Rome, Gaius Julius Caesar, is preparing for war in Parthia.* If the campaign succeeds, Caesar will have conquered more territory than Alexander the Great.

There is a prophecy that only a king can conquer Parthia, so before he sets off, Caesar will be crowned King of Rome on the Ides of March.

Rome has been further disturbed by rumors that Caesar plans to move the entire capital to Alexandria and start a Roman/Egyptian Empire, with Cleopatra as his queen and Caesarion as his heir.

INSIDE: EDITORIAL - Who does Caesar think he is? The Espresso says, No kings in Rome!

* Afghanistan and neighboring countries

Things are getting nasty around here.

The streets are full of small groups of people muttering under their breath. The gossip among the slaves is that Brutus and his brother-in-law, Cassius, are having secret meetings in dark corners. Even JC has noticed this. He said to me the other day that Cassius was looking very pale. "What do you think he's up to?" he asked.

As we came through the Forum this afternoon, one of the Soothsayers, Spurinna, called out, "Caesar, beware the Ides of March!" JC ignored him; he doesn't believe in prophecies.

I'm the same. How can you tell the future by looking at birds in flight or the way that chickens eat their food?!

Some people even think they can tell the future by looking at the guts of bulls, goats, and sheep! They split the animal's stomach open, pull out the intestines, liver, and kidneys, look at the way they lie, and then say what's going to happen.

If I did that, I'd know what was going to happen in the near future—I'd lose my lunch!

THE IDES OF MARCH

Maybe I am starting to believe in omens! And after last night, who could blame me?

First of all, Lepidus* came to dinner and told JC that his horses were refusing to eat and were shedding tears.

After dinner, the men started talking about death and the best way to die. JC said he would like his death to be "sudden and unexpected." I don't know why, but I felt a shiver run right up my spine.

Soon after JC went to bed, all the doors and windows burst open as if blown by a sudden gale. Then Calphurnia woke up screaming because she'd had a nightmare that JC had been murdered.

* Caesar's Master of Horse, who went on to rule Rome with Mark Antony and Octavius

This morning, Calphurnia begged JC not to go to the Senate. JC was pretty nervous himself, though he tried not to show it, so he gave in and sent for Mark Antony to make his excuses.

Then Brutus and Cassius showed up with JC's pal General Decimus. When JC told them he'd decided to stay at home, they mocked him. Was JC frightened by a woman's nightmares and the ravings of false prophets? So in the end, JC said he'd go.

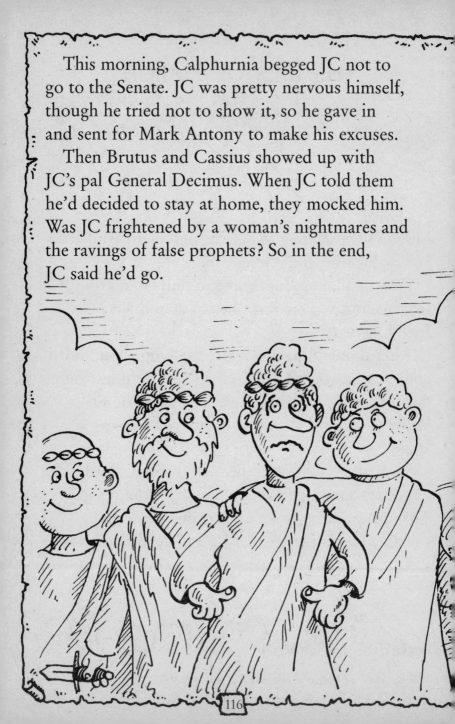

Before we went to the Forum, I happened to glance at the astrology page in the local newspaper.

ESPRESSO HOROSCOPE YOUR STARS FOR THE IDES OF MARCH WITH MYSTA MEGA

HAVING LOOKED INTO MY CRYSTAL INTESTINES I CAN SEE THE FOLLOWING:

- Watch your back if you are named Caesar
- Warning: Don't go out today if your name is Julius
- Anyone with the initials JC should be very careful
- People whom you consider your friends may let you down today
- Don't let anyone with the name Brutus near you for the next 24 hours
- The Forum could be a dangerous place
- Try to avoid daggers—they can hurt
- WATCH IT, CAESAR!

Call me silly, but I've got a hunch that something might happen.

The Forum, Rome

When we got to the Forum, JC was stopped by
Artemidorus, who's one of his secretaries and a
friend of Inkus Fingus. Artemidorus gave JC a
note and asked him to read it before he was
hustled away by a couple of nasty-looking thugs.
JC just passed the note to me without looking at
it. He said, "Take care of this, Commonus," and
went in.

I was curious to see what Artemidorus wanted,
so I opened the note and read it. It said:

Dear Caesar,
i hope you are well. Brutus, Cassius, and
several others are going to kill you when
you go to the Senate today.
Best Wishes,
Artemidorus

I tore the note into little pieces. Well, why not?
Slaves have to do as they're told, but you show me
where it says they have to do their bosses any
favors.

When I reached the Senate, I was just in time to see Metellus Cimber tear JC's cloak from his shoulders. This must have been a signal. Another half dozen men drew daggers.

JC cried, "But this is violence!" No kidding, I thought.

Another man, Casca, stabbed JC in the shoulder. He cried, "Casca, you villain, what are you doing?" It seemed obvious to me.

Cassius was next. He stabbed JC, and there was a terrible struggle.

Eventually, JC fell to his knees before the statue of Pompey. He looked up and saw Brutus with a knife in his hand.

"You, too, my son?" he said. Then he pulled his cloak over his head, just as Pompey had done before him.

Et tu, Brute?

Half of Rome is in flames.

Since JC's death, a great fiery ball* has appeared, crossing the night sky. The people believe this is JC's spirit taking its place among the gods. I hope he remembered to take Teddus.

Brutus and his cronies fled after Mark Antony read Caesar's will. Before he died, everyone wanted JC's blood; but when they found out that he'd left three gold coins to every citizen, people started saying that he wasn't such a bad guy, and they began yelling for the blood of the people who had killed him. Typical.

Anyway, nobody's worried about a runaway slave in all the confusion, so I've managed to stow away on a barge going downriver to the coast. I'll hitch a ride with one of the boats trading tin with my own country. With any luck, I'll be home by summer.

*A comet appeared in the sky over Rome following Caesar's death.

Brittania. The Country of the Dumnonii

The voyage took longer than I expected, but I got home this morning just as the first leaves were starting to fall.

I shouted, "Sciatica! Darling! I'm home!"

She turned around from the fire. "Oh, there you are! Do you know what time it is? Where have you been? Oh, you've been with the Roman army, have you? All right, tell the truth. What have you been up to?..."

I sat in my favorite chair and put my feet up with a contented sigh.

It was good to be back.

The End of the Roman Republic

After Caesar's death, Rome was plunged into thirteen years of civil war.

Mark Antony, Lepidus, and Octavius formed a Triumvirate. They defeated Brutus and Cassius, who committed suicide at the battle of Philippi in 42 BC.

Cleopatra left Rome for Alexandria. She tried to regain control of Egypt with Mark Antony. Defeated by Octavius, they too committed suicide.

The republic had ended forever. Following his victory, Octavius became the Emperor Augustus, the first of the Roman Emperors.

Historical Note
By R. Celavie, Professor of History
at the University of Hard Knocks, Peoria

Having examined this book thoroughly, I am sorry to report that once again Barlow and Skidmore have succeeded in conning their innocent publishers.

As usual, the main events are recorded accurately; but also, as usual, the book is riddled with inaccuracies:

• Newspapers and information hotlines did not exist in Roman times.

• How on Earth could an ancient Briton like Commonus know the language of nuclear warfare? (*Intercontinental ballistic tizzy* and *ground zero*, indeed!)

• For that matter, how could Commonus, living in a country where literacy was virtually unknown, have learned to read and write in his own language, Latin, and the language of Gaul?

• Teddy bears were named after President Theodore Roosevelt; it is impossible for Caesar to have had one (no matter how insecure he was).

Furthermore, I have not been able to find any one of the so-called panel of experts Barlow and Skidmore claim to have contacted to prove the diary's authenticity. I am convinced that this Lost Diary, like previous ones, is a clever forgery.

Publishers' Note:

Barlow and Skidmore, you're dead!

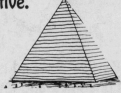